CLASSICAL PIANO SOLOS COLLECTION

VOLUME FOUR

Wise Publications
London/New York/Paris/Sydney/Copenhagen/Madrid

Exclusive Distributors:

Music Sales Limited
8/9 Frith Street, London W1V 5TZ, England.

Music Sales Pty Limited
120 Rothschild Avenue, Rosebery, NSW 2018, Australia.

Music Sales Corporation
257 Park Avenue South, New York, NY10010, United States of America.

Order No. AM91537
ISBN 0-7119-3759-1
This book © Copyright 1994 by Wise Publications

Book design by Studio Twenty, London
Computer management by Adam Hay Editorial Design
Compiled by Stephen Harding

Printed in the United Kingdom by
J.B. Offset Printers (Marks Tey) Limited, Marks Tey, Essex.

YOUR GUARANTEE OF QUALITY

As publishers, we strive to produce every book to the highest commercial standards.
This book has been carefully designed to minimise awkward page turns and to make
playing from it a real pleasure.
Particular care has been given to specifying acid-free, neutral-sized paper made from pulps
which have not been elemental chlorine bleached. This pulp is from farmed sustainable forests
and was produced with special regard for the environment.
Throughout, the printing and binding have been planned to ensure a sturdy,
attractive publication which should give years of enjoyment.
If your copy fails to meet our high standards, please inform us and
we will gladly replace it.

Music Sales' complete catalogue describes thousands of titles and
is available in full colour sections by subject, direct from Music Sales Limited.
Please state your areas of interest and send a cheque/postal order for £1.50 for postage to:
Music Sales Limited, Newmarket Road, Bury St. Edmunds, Suffolk IP33 3YB.

Allegro from Suite No.7 George Frideric Handel **24**

Bagatelle in A Major, Op.33, No.4 Ludwig van Beethoven **6**

Bell Ringing, Op.54, No.6 Edvard Grieg **22**

Canon César Franck **15**

Feuillet d'Album, Op.19, No.3 Peter Ilyich Tchaikovsky **46**

Humoresque, Op.101, No.7 Antonin Dvořák **18**

Impromptu in A♭, Op.142/D.935, No.2 Franz Schubert **42**

Intermezzo in B♭ Minor, Op.117, No.2 Johannes Brahms **10**

Invention No.8 in F Major, BWV779 Johann Sebastian Bach **4**

Mazurka in B♭ Major, Op.7, No.1 Frédéric Chopin **16**

Mouvement Perpetuel No.1 Francis Poulenc **40**

Nuages Gris Franz Liszt **34**

Of Foreign Lands And People - No.1 from Scenes Of Childhood Robert Schumann **48**

Piano Sonata in E♭ Major, Hob.XVI:49 - 1st Movement Joseph Haydn **26**

Piano Sonata in G, K283 - 1st Movement Wolfgang Amadeus Mozart **36**

Piano Sonata No.9 in E Major, Op.14, No.1 - 2nd Movement Ludwig van Beethoven **8**

Prelude in E Minor, Op.11, No.4 Alexander Scriabin **33**

Invention No.8 in F Major
BWV779

Composed by Johann Sebastian Bach

Bagatelle in A major
Op.33, No.4

Composed by Ludwig van Beethoven

Piano Sonata No.9 in E Major
Op.14, No.1 - 2nd Movement

Composed by Ludwig van Beethoven

Allegretto

Maggiore

[legato]

Allegretto da capo
sin' al Maggiore,
e poi la Coda.

Coda

Intermezzo in B♭ Minor
Op.117, No.2

Composed by Johannes Brahms

Andante non troppo e con molta espressione

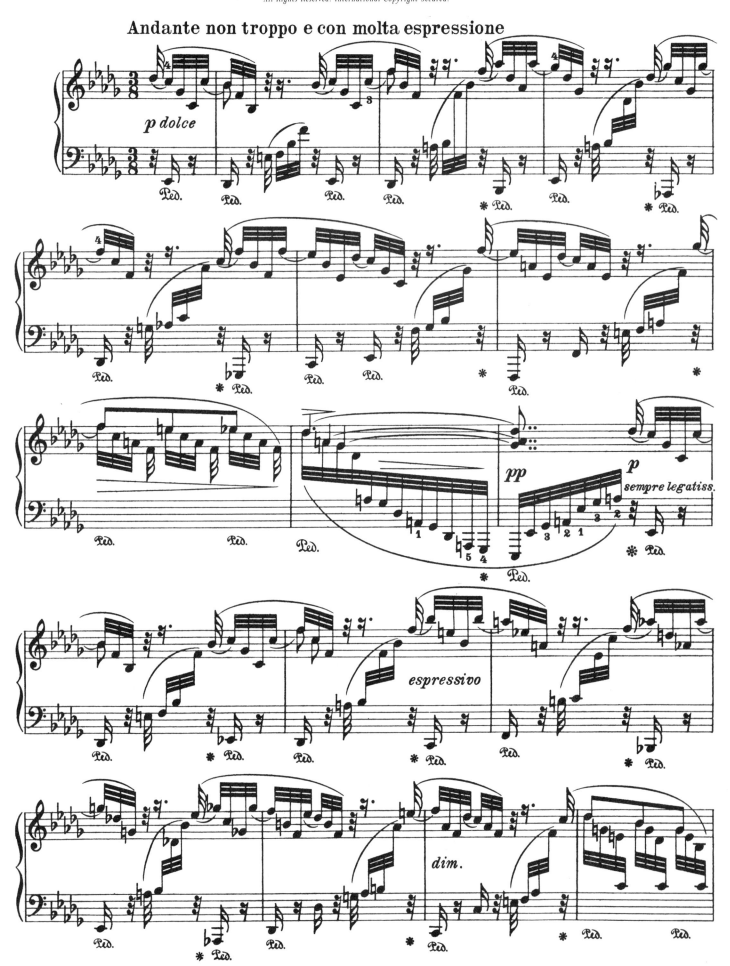

Canon

Composed by César Franck

Poco allegretto

Mazurka in B♭ Major
Op.7, No.1

Composed by Frédéric Chopin

Humoresque
Op.101, No.7

Composed by Antonin Dvořák

Bell Ringing
Op. 54, No. 6
Composed by Edvard Grieg

Allegro
from Suite No. 7
Composed by George Frideric Handel

Piano Sonata in E♭ Major
Hob.XVI:49 - 1st Movement

Composed by Joseph Haydn

Allegro [non troppo]

Prelude in E Minor
Op.11, No.4

Composed by Alexander Scriabin

Nuages Gris

Composed by Franz Liszt

(poco a poco agitato)

sempre legato
ped. simile)

(calmando)

rall.

p

35

Piano Sonata in G
K283 - 1st Movement

Composed by Wolfgang Amadeus Mozart

Allegro

Mouvement Perpetuel No.1

Composed by Francis Poulenc

En général, sans nuances, beaucoup de pédale

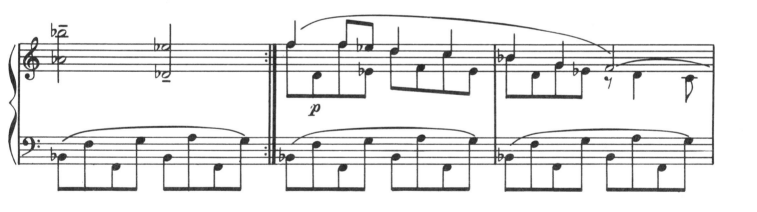

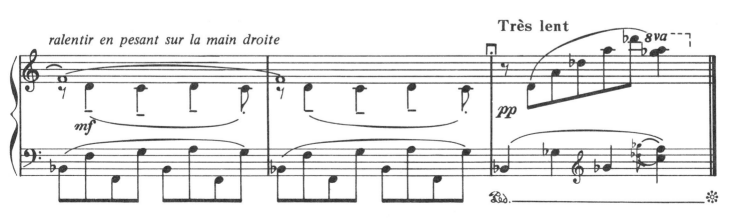

Impromptu in A♭
Op.142/D.935, No.2

Composed by Franz Schubert

Feuillet d'Album
Op.19, No.3

Composed by Peter Ilyich Tchaikovsky

Allegretto semplice

47

Of Foreign Lands And People - No.1
from Scenes Of Childhood

Composed by Robert Schumann